CARTOON NETWORK

PANINI BOOKS

Cartoon Network Annual 2008 is published under license by Panini Publishing, a division of Panini UK Limited. Office of publication: Panini House, Coach & Horses Passage, The Pantiles, Tunbridge Wells, Kent, TN2 5UJ. This publication may not be sold, except by authorised dealers, and is sold subject to the condition that it shall not be sold or distributed with any part of its cover or markings removed, nor in a mutilated condition. Printed in Italy. ISBN: 978-1-84653-029-6
Editor: Alexandra Hain-Cole, Designer: Melanie Wilson

£6.99

Welcome

Step into the jam-packed world of toons with the 2008 Cartoon Network Annual! There are more of them in the mix than ever so dive in and get ready for a bellyful of serious silliness! Enjoy!

Your Guide...

MEET... Ed, Edd n Eddy ™

They're the greatest gruesome threesome that the world has ever seen, so let's get down to business and make their acquaintance!

Ed

TRADEMARK: His impressive monobrow.
HOMETOWN: Peach Creek
HOBBIES: Model making, 'watching B' movies, scratching his various rashes.
FAVOURITE FOOD: Jawbreaker candy.
WORST TRAIT: His ability to attract flies due to his lack of personal hygiene. Yuck.

Eddy

TRADEMARK: The dollar-shaped glint in his eye.
HOMETOWN: Peach Creek
HOBBIES: Making money, coming up with scams, fleecing money from his friends, dreaming of money – all things money-related, basically.
FAVOURITE FOOD: Jawbreaker candy.
WORST TRAIT: He's a natural leader but he sometimes puts the others in danger on his madcapped money-making missions!

Edd

TRADEMARK: His sharp mind and nervous expression.
HOMETOWN: Peach Creek
HOBBIES: Making lists, organising things, nuclear physics, trying to keep the others out of trouble – and failing!
FAVOURITE FOOD: Jawbreaker candy.
WORST TRAIT: Double-D finds it hard to laugh at himself – or anyone else, for that matter.

A SPOONFUL OF ED

JONO HOWARD
WRITING
CORY TOOMEY
PENCILING
ANGUS BUNGAY
INKING
NICK J. NAPOLITANO
LETTERING
HEROIC AGE
COLORING
RACHEL GLUCKSTERN
ASST. EDITING
JOAN HILTY
EDITING

GOOD GRACIOUS, ED! THE CONDITION OF YOUR TEETH IS *DEPLORABLE!*

YEAH, *MUNGMOUTH!* IT'S LIKE A ROW OF *GRAVESTONES* IN THERE! WHEN WAS THE LAST TIME YOU *BRUSHED?*

AS YOU CAN SEE, EDDY...ED'S *LACK* OF *HYGIENE* HAS LED TO A *PLETHORA* OF *CAVITIES* AND *DECAY!*

SQUEEK

SO LUMPY'S HEAD IS *ROTTING?* WHAT'S YOUR *POINT?* THERE AIN'T NO MONEY...

...IN PEOPLE'S *TEETH!*

RINSE... AND *SPIT,* ED!

SPLOOSH

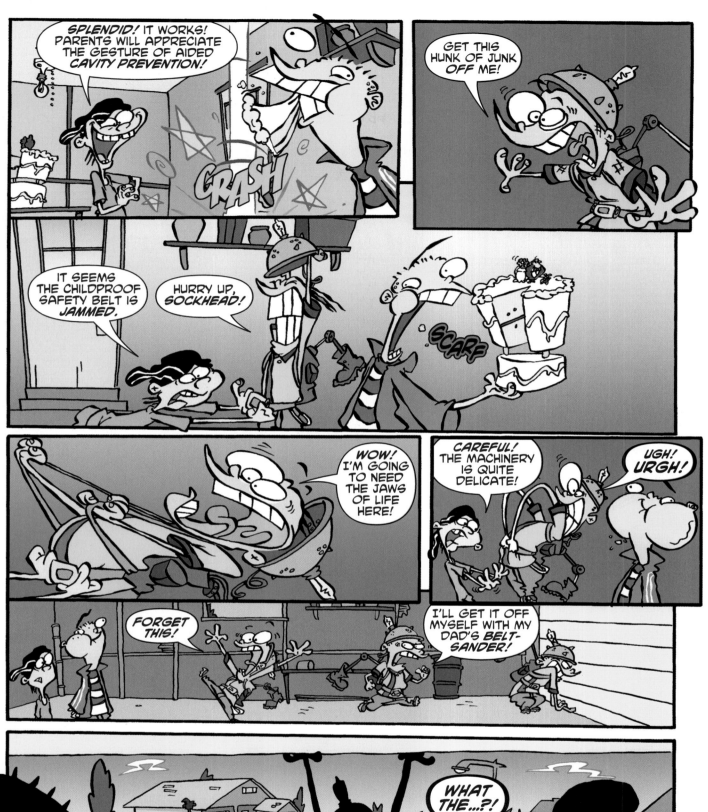

HOW TO DRAW...
Robotboy™

JUST FOLLOW THESE FIVE SIMPLE STEPS TO DRAW THE SUPER-ACTIVATING SUPER FERO, ROBOTBOY.

1 Start by drawing a circle for the head and a smaller circle for the belly. For the body and legs, draw a triangle.

2 Add the ear, which is shaped like a paper cup, then draw the two leg shapes. Remember to use the triangle as a guide.

3 Draw in the hand and the leg details to form his boots and gloves.

4 Imagine his head like a football and place the eyes in the bottom half. Then draw in the ear highlights.

5 Once you've added the mouth, he's finished and ready to super-activate into action.

A Grim ADVENTURE!

The Grim Adventures of Billy & Mandy

Help Grim, Billy and Mandy to get back to Endsville safely as they battle bad guys and get into a series of scrapes! Play the game with a friend - all you need is a die and some counters.

START

1 Stop to grab some cookies. Miss a turn.

2

3 Grim loses his scythe. Miss a turn to find it.

4

5

6 Mandy decides to change direction. Go back two spaces.

7

8

9

10 You win a limbo contest. Move forward three spaces.

11

12

13 Billy covers your map with snot. Miss a turn.

14

15

16 You are turned into a monster. Miss a turn while you wait to go back to normal.

17

18 Billy spots a spider. Run to space 21.

19

20 You bump into Irwin. Miss a turn while you catch up.

21

22

23 Mandy remembers a cunning shortcut. Roll again.

24

25

26 You get trapped in the Underworld. Throw an even number to escape.

FINIS

ENDSVILL

14

SCOTT CUNNINGHAM—WRITER
ROBERT POPE—PENCILLER
PHIL MOY—INKER
TRAVIS LANHAM—LETTERER
HEROIC AGE—COLORIST
RACHEL GLUCKSTERN—ASST. EDITOR
JOAN HILTY—EDITOR
GRIM ADVENTURES OF BILLY & MANDY
CREATED BY MAXWELL ATOMS

WELL, *I'M OUTTA* HERE!

I'VE NEVER SEEN SUCH A *STUPID SHOW*, EXCEPT FOR MAYBE "COMPLETELY OCCUPIED YURT."

THERE'S SOME PAINT DRYING IN THE NEXT ROOM, BILLY. WE'RE GOING TO GO WATCH *THAT* FOR A WHILE.

DID... YOU... SAY... SOMETHING...

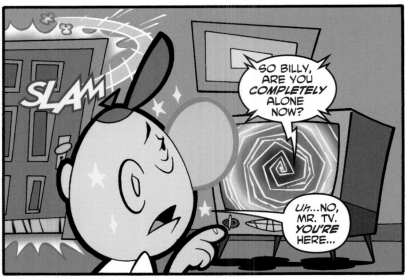

SLAM

SO BILLY, ARE YOU *COMPLETELY* ALONE NOW?

Uh...NO, MR. TV. *YOU'RE* HERE...

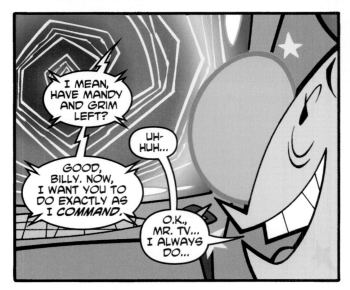

I MEAN, HAVE MANDY AND GRIM LEFT?

UH-HUH...

GOOD, BILLY. NOW, I WANT YOU TO DO EXACTLY AS I *COMMAND*.

O.K., MR. TV... I ALWAYS DO...

FIRST, *EXIT* THE *HOUSE*, USING THE *BACK* DOOR. THEN *CROSS* THE *STREET* AND GO TO *THIS* ADDRESS...

BUT TV, SHOULDN'T I *STAND UP* FIRST?

YES, BILLY. STAND UP FIRST.

HEY, THE FLOOR'S *SLIPPERY!* LIKE SOMEONE'S *DROOLED* ALL OVER IT!

SPLOOSH

I CAN'T BELIEVE YOU DID *ALL THIS*-- THE TV STUDIO, THE GIANT HYPNO-WHEEL, THE SPECIAL SECRET BROADCAST-- JUST SO YOU COULD *CONTROL BILLY'S MIND!*

UNTIL A HALF HOUR AGO, *I CONTROLLED BILLY'S MIND,* AND LET ME TELL YOU, *IT'S NOT WORTH IT!*

WAIT, MANDY, I'M SORRY!

COME ON, BILLY!

MAYBE YOU'D LIKE TO WATCH SOME "COMPLETELY OCCUPIED YURT," BOY?

OH, MAN, MANDY WILL PROBABLY *NEVER* MARRY ME NOW.

RUSTLE RUSTLE

HEY, WHAT'S THAT *SOUND?*

MUST... OBEY... MUST... OBEY... MUST... OBEY... MUST... OBEY...

§Snicker§ WHAT DID THAT DOOFUS THINK? THAT ONLY *ONE* BILLY LIVED IN ENDSVILLE?

MUST... OBEY... *MANDY.*

END

MENTAL ARTS

He may be the master of martial arts but Samurai Jack has a few problems, mainly thanks to his evil nemesis, Aku. Can you give him a helping hand on his tactical trail to victory?

LIAR, LIAR

Aku is trying to foil Samurai Jack by feeding him false truths. Can you spot the only fact in this list of lies?

1. AKU IS AN OLD WOMAN IN DISGUISE.
2. THE SCOTSMAN IS FROM TURKEY.
3. JACK TRAINED AS A BALLET DANCER BEFORE BEING INTRODUCED TO MARTIAL ARTS.
4. JACK'S REAL NAME ISN'T JACK.
5. THE JAPANESE WORD FOR SAMURAI SWORD IS KRUMPETO.

SAMURAI SKILLS

Can you spot which of these items Samurai Jack wouldn't need in his quest to destroy the sorcerous snake, Aku?

A
D
B
C
E
G
F
H

21

CAMP LAZO PHOTO FINISH!

The residents of Camp Kidney have just finished their most gruelling test – the Beanscout Assault Course Race. It's down to a photo finish but someone's tampered with the snaps! Can you spot the 8 changes and tell who won the race?

THE PERFECT VERY HEAVY DRIZZLE

BOBBY LONDON
WRITER

MIKE KAZALEH
ARTIST

MIKE SELLERS
LETTERER

HEROIC AGE
COLORIST

RACHEL GLUCKSTERN
ASST. EDITOR

JOAN HILTY
EDITOR

STOP HIM, LAZLO, BEFORE HE RUINS *ANOTHER* PERFECTLY GOOD DAY!

2,240 HOURS IN THIS CABIN HAS DRIVEN HIM NUTS!

YEAH!

NEITHER OF *US* SMELL ANYTHING.

CHIP AND SKIP HAVE A POINT, RAJ. WE'VE BEEN COOPED UP IN HERE AN AWFULLY LONG TIME. BESIDES...

...THE CAMP'S LAUNDRY CABIN IS ON TOP OF A HILL, AND THE NONSTOP RAIN IS CAUSING LEAKY LAKE TO RISE. *IT'S AN IMPOSSIBLE TASK!*

LAUNDRY

I DO NOT CARE WHAT YOU SAY, I WILL NOT BRING *SHAME* UPON MY ANCESTORS!

WHY NOT?

WE DO IT ALL THE TIME.

THAT IS BECAUSE YOU ARE DISGUSTING *DUNG BEETLES* WITH *NO* PERSONAL HYGIENE! NOW, LEAVE ME ALONE. I AM OFF TO SEEK MY *DESTINY!*

BUT RAJ...

SUDSO

LET HIM GO, LAZLO!

HE'S STIR CRAZY.

MAYBE YOU GUYS SHOULD GO BACK TO YOUR OWN CABIN.

YOUR OWN CABIN!

27

The End.

EVIL UNITED

Yes, it is I, Mojo Jojo, the terror of Townsville. Those ridiculous Powerpuff Girls are attempting to solve a mystery which I myself have created... Help them to uncover the truth at your own peril. Mwa-ha-ha-ha-ha!

I have chosen a villainous ally to remove the Mayor for good. Can you see who from my cunning clues?

CLUES

They are not wearing dungarees, just as I am not.

They do not have luscious locks of dark hair, more's the pity.

My evil ally is not as green as I myself am.

They are not wearing hats, unlike myself.

FUZZY LUMPKINS

LITTLE ARTURO

SNAKE

GRUBBER

THE AMEOBA BOYS

HIM

BIG BILLY

SEDUSA

Who is the chosen villain? Find out on page 61.

29

STRIP SHOW — JOHNNY BRAVO

...JOHNNY, NO WOMAN CAN RESIST HIM. HE'S...

JOHNNY BRAVO in BODY Beautiful: SPINELESS

HEALTH CLUB

STROM	POPE	ALBRECHT	LOPEZ	SNO CONE	RICHARDS	HILTY
writer	penciller	inker	letterer	colorist	ass't editor	editor

JOHNNY BRAVO created by VAN PARTIBLE

HOWDY, PARDNER! BECAUSE YOU **DEMANDED** IT, **JOHNNY** IS BACK WITH MORE WORKOUT TIPS FOR THE **ROMANTICALLY INCLINED!**

SURPRISINGLY, MOST LOVER-BOYS DON'T KNOW WHERE TO BEGIN WHEN IT COMES TO **EXERCISE!**

TAKE MY PAL **CARL** HERE, FOR EXAMPLE. TSK! HE'S GOT IT ALL **WRONG.** WHAT HE SHOULD BE WORKING ON IS HIS **SPINE!**

GRUNT! **WHAT?!?** YOU'RE **NUTS!**

NO WAY, JUNIOR! THE **SPINE** IS THE TRUE **MUSCLE OF LOVE!**

YEAH? LIKE HOW?

THINK ABOUT IT—

—IT TAKES **BACKBONE** TO CALL A GIRL FOR THE FIRST TIME! GRUNT! IT TAKES **BACKBONE** TO ASK FOR A DATE! HUFF! AND THAT'S JUST THE **BEGINNING!** WHEEZE! THERE ARE A **MILLION** USES FOR A **STRONG BACK!**

SUCH AS?

HAVEN'T YOU HEARD? NGH! **CHIVALRY** ISN'T DEAD!

I SEE...!

END

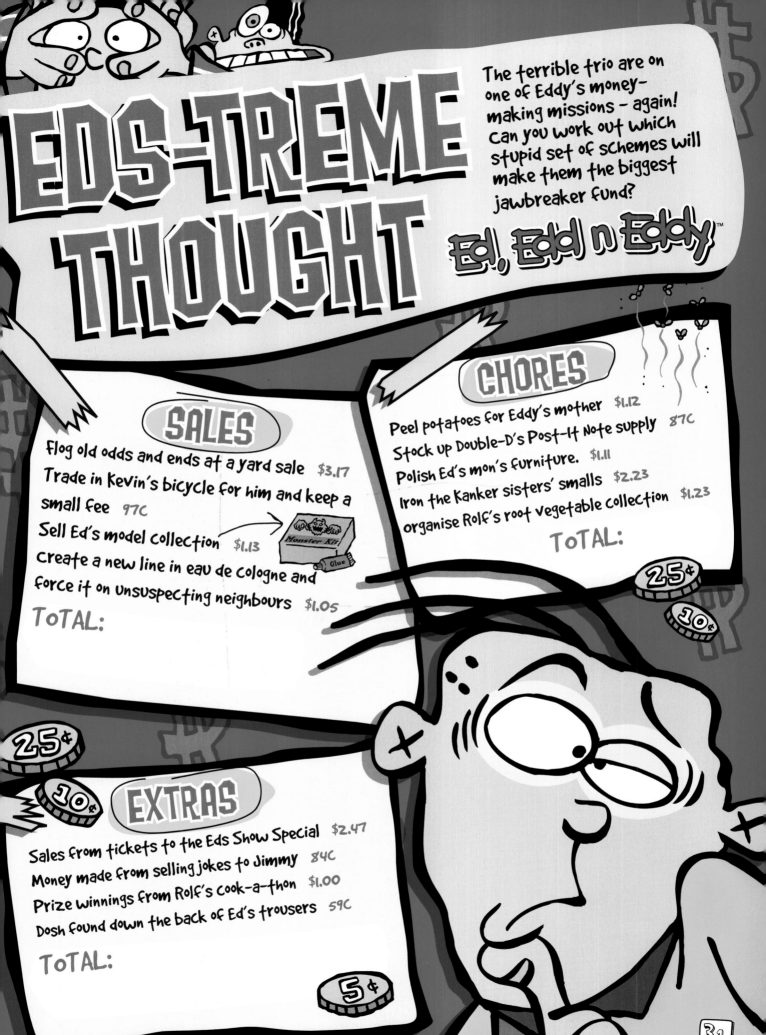

BEN 10 TASK TIME!

Ben Tennyson may have superpowers and freaky abilities coming out of his ears but that doesn't mean that he's a puzzle genius. He's going to need your help to work his way through these...

ALIEN ANSWERS

All of these alien alter egos fit into the grid, you just have to work out where!

XLR8
Upgrade
Fourarms
Ripjaw
Diamondhead
Ghostfreak
Wildmutt
Heatblast
Greymatter
Stinkfly

F	O	U	R	A	R	M	S	T	G	D
K	8	G	A	R	F	E	N	T	R	I
A	T	P	9	S	2	L	S	U	6	A
E	I	W	C	H	U	5	W	M	A	M
R	I	P	J	A	W	E	K	D	H	O
F	4	L	U	N	I	3	F	L	Y	N
T	D	X	L	R	8	Q	E	I	S	D
S	O	M	J	Z	B	K	I	W	I	H
O	7	E	D	A	R	G	P	U	X	E
H	E	A	T	B	L	A	S	T	O	A
G	R	E	Y	M	A	T	T	E	R	D

WATCH IT!

Ben's watch is seriously misbehaving - it keeps scrambling up all of his alien DNA superheroes. Can you work out which is which, and who's missing from the mix?

yfkniist

utliwdtm

hddaen omiad

bianettas

ttryga meer

wapjri

LR8X

rarmus fo

deupgra

Wildmutt
Upgrade
Four Arms
Grey matter
XLR8
Ghostreak
Diamondhead
Ripjaws
Stinkfly
Heatblast

32

STRIP SHOW

BEN 10

BEN 10 FAST LANE

MAN OF ACTION writer DARIO BRIZUELA artist
STUDIO 1137 letterer HEROIC AGE colorist
RACHEL GLUCKSTERN asst. editor JOAN HILTY editor
BEN 10 created by MAN OF ACTION

DCCNA14

THEY'RE *AMAZING*, GRADY! HOW FAST ARE THEY GOING?

UP TO TWO HUNDRED AND TEN MILES AN HOUR, GWEN!

MY OLD FRIEND *GRADY* WAS NICE ENOUGH TO INVITE US.

I THOUGHT YOU MIGHT APPRECIATE A LITTLE FUEL-INJECTED FUN AFTER MONDAY'S DEBACLE AT THE LOUISIANAN *ANT FARM.*

WHAT DO *YOU* THINK, BEN?

...I THINK MY EARS ARE BLEEDING.

DON'T TELL ME YOU'RE *BORED*, BEN? LOOK AT THOSE FEATS OF HUMAN ENGINEERING! IT TAKES A LOT OF *SKILL* TO BE A RACECAR DRIVER!

SKILL? ALL THEY DO IS DRIVE AROUND IN A CIRCLE!

SHOOTING STAR

VROOM

WOW-- 218.432 SECONDS! THAT'S A TRACK RECORD!

BILL ELLIOT ONLY DID *210.386*, AND THAT WAS *BEFORE* THE CARBURETOR RESTRICTIONS--

HOW COULD YOU EVEN POSSIBLY KNOW THAT? YOU'RE A *GIRL*!

SHE'S RIGHT, BEN! AND ON ANY OTHER DAY THAT WOULD BE A TRACK RECORD, BUT TODAY, WE'RE JUST LUCKY

HUH? YOU'VE GOT THE FINEST CAR OUT HERE. WHAT ELSE COULD POSSIBLY GO UP AGAINST HER?

RUUUMBLE

--UH, WHAT IS *THAT*!

SPEAK OF THE DEVIL... AND HE SHOWS HIS TAILPIPE.

THE END

MEGA MIX-UP!

IN BITS!

MEGAS may be an XLR (eXtra Large Robot) but that doesn't mean that he's indestructable - just look what Coop's done to him! Can you help Coop work out which pieces aren't part of MEGAS?

IN DISGUISE

Commander Kiva Andrew has made copies of MEGAS to fool the Glorft. Can you work out which is the true XLR?

-ORIGINAL-

-FACT FILE-

NAME: MEGAS (Mechanised Earth Attack System)

DESCRIPTION: Futuristic prototype giant robot

CREATED BY: The alien race of Glorft

PILOT: Coop Cooplowski and Commander Kiva Andrew

FAST FACTS

So he's got the powers of ten alien beings, but what does that actually mean? And how does that fit in with being a regular ten year old kid? Read on and find out...

>>> PROFILE

NAME: Ben Tennyson
AGE: 10
HOBBIES: Playing computer games (particularly Sumo Slammer), riding his bike, playing the drums, saving the world.
FAMILY: Grandpa Max and one cousin, Gwen.

>>> THE OMNITRIX

Ben's powers come from an extra-terrestrial watch-like device called the Omnitrix. Ben can access ten alien forms and as each of these has its own special abilities and he can change between them as he likes, he has a huge variety of superhuman powers. He takes his powers seriously, but that doesn't mean he can't get up to a little superpowered mischief every now and then!

>>> FOES

KEVIN II

Kevin may look like a rebellious 11 year old but he actually has the unique ability to absorb any type of energy and release it at will. When absorbing energy from the Omnitrix's aliens, he becomes an incomplete, but effective, version of that alien, making it hard for Ben to defeat him.

VILGAX

The evil Vilgax is a Chimera Sui Generis from a place called the Shadowy Realm. A vicious, intergalactic conqueror, Vilgax will stop at nothing to obtain the Omnitrix and use it to build an army capable of conquering every planet in the galaxy.

...XLR8...

POWERS: Can run at 300 MPH on any surface, even ice.

...WILDMUTT...

POWERS: Heightened senses and the ability to fire harmful quills from his back.

...DIAMONDHEAD...

POWERS: Harder than diamond and able to cut through any surface.

...GREYMATTER...

POWERS: A tiny genius who can master any complex weapon within seconds.

...FOURARMS...

POWERS: 12 feet tall, super-strong and covered in armour. A natural born fighter.

...UPGRADE...

POWERS: Able to transform into any mechanical device.

...HEATBLAST...

POWERS: Comes from the sun and is able to blast bolts of fire from his arms and mouth and is completely invincible in fire.

...GHOSTFREAK...

POWERS: Has ghostly powers, including the ability to walk through walls, invisibility and a terrifying appearance.

...RIPJAW...

POWERS: An expert swimmer who has powerful claws and a devastating bite.

...STINKFLY...

POWERS: Expert flyer with pincers and a deathly tail.

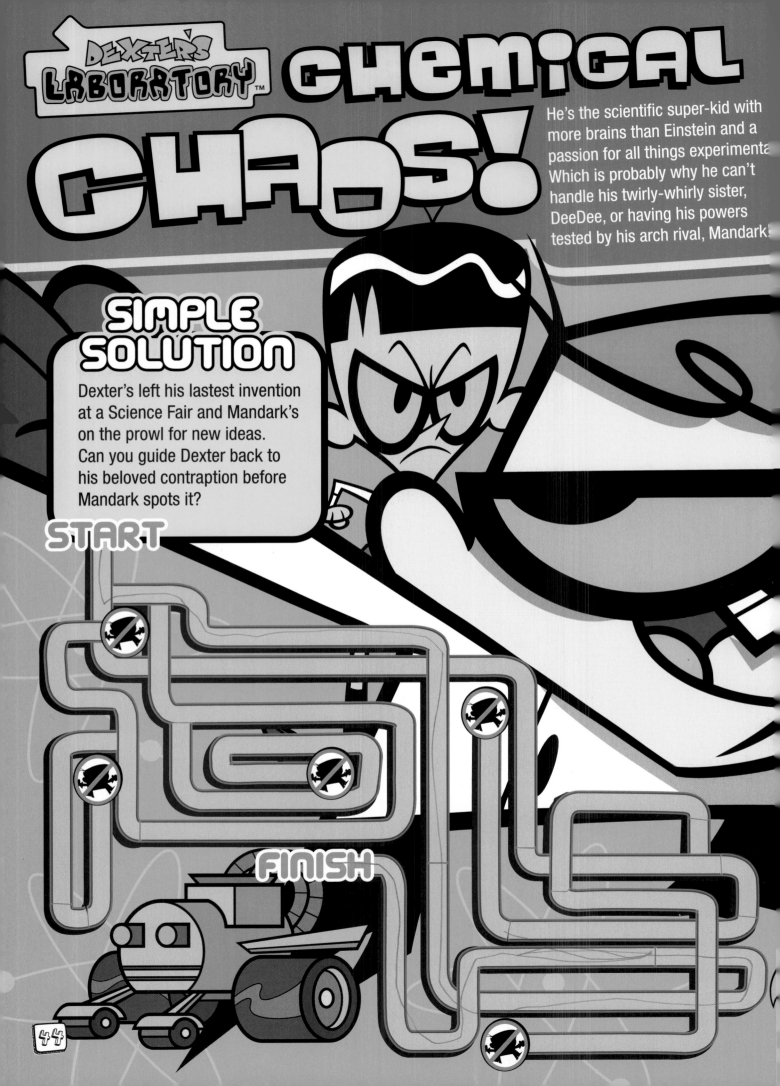

MISTAKEN IDENTITY

An unfortunate accident in the laboratory has led to the cloning of Dexter, DeeDee and Mandark. The only trouble is that the likeness is not quite right. Can you spot the seven differences between these two shots of them to save the original trio from destruction?

THE BIG BANG!

Dexter's banned his sister from his lab - for good reason! She's been mixing his chemicals and a reaction may lead them to explode... Can you work out which two chemicals she could safely mix? Think quickly!

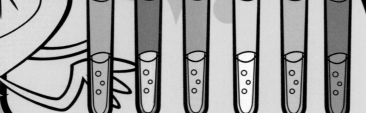

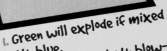

1. Green will explode if mixed with blue.
2. Red and purple both blow-up if added to yellow.
3. Orange cannot be combined with anything else.
4. Yellow and green are a toxic mix.
5. Purple and green should not be seen.
6. Red and purple? No way!
7. Red won't go with green, purple or blue.
8. Blue and purple spell trouble.

"MY NAME IS *DEXTER.* I AM *BROADCASTING* FROM THE PLANET *EARTH*, WHICH IS THE *THIRD* PLANET ORBITING THE *STAR* KNOWN AS *SOL*, OR TO DOPES LIKE MY *STOOPID* SISTER, DEE-DEE, THE *SUN.*

"I AM SEEKING ANY *NON-HOSTILE,* INTELLIGENT BEINGS FROM OTHER WORLDS WHO MIGHT BE INTERESTED IN THE *EXCHANGE OF SCIENTIFIC INFORMATION.*

VISITORS FROM SPACE

John Rozum – Writer   John Delaney – Penciller   Jeff Albrecht – Inker   Dexter's Laboratory created by Genndy Tartakovsky

Travis Lanham – Letterer   Heroic Age – Colorist   Rachel Gluckstern – Asst. Editor   Joan Hilty – Editor

"IS *ANYONE* OUT THERE?"

I REPEAT, IS ANYONE OUT THERE?

GREETINGS, DEXTER OF EARTH. I AM *FFLONNPHROGG* OF *DIMNINUUTI*. THIS IS MY SCIENTIFIC ADVISOR, *SQUEEMONOGG*.

GREETINGS, DEXTER OF EARTH.

AM I TO DEDUCE THAT *YOU* ARE THE *LEADING SCIENTIST* OF EARTH?

IF THERE IS ANOTHER, WHOSE *GENIUS RIVALS* MY *OWN*, I AM UNAWARE OF THEM. ⸘Heh-heh⸘

AFTER ALL, IT TOOK THE *GENIUS* OF *DEXTER* TO CONTACT YOU, DID IT--

YOO-HOO! WHATCHA DOING, DEXTER?

WHAT IS *THAT?*

⸘Heh-heh⸘ THAT IS *NOTHING.* JUST IGNORE HER. THAT IS WHAT *I* DO.

WE RECOGNIZE THAT THIS CALL IS *NOT* INEXPENSIVE, SO LET US GET RIGHT DOWN TO BUSINESS. WHAT SORT OF SCIENTIFIC KNOWLEDGE DO YOU HOPE TO EXCHANGE WITH US?

WELL, AS YOU CAN SEE, MY LABORA--

YOO-HOO! WHATSAMATTER, DEXTER, CAN'T YOU *HEAR* ME *WAY UP THERE?*

OOOH! WHATCHA *WATCHING*, DEXTER?

PLEASE EXCUSE ME FOR ONE MOMENT?

PERHAPS YOU WILL BE INTERESTED IN MY *GIANT PARTICLE RANDOMIZER.* IT HAS...

WE ALREADY HAVE ONE.

HMMM

PERHAPS, THEN, YOU WILL FIND MY *NEUTRON MICROSCOPE,* WHICH HAS THE CAPABILITY OF PEERING INTO THE *SUB-SUB-ATOMIC--*

PLEASE, EVERY *SCHOOL CHILD* ON DIMNINUUTI HAS ONE OF THOSE, IN A MORE PRACTICAL AND ECONOMICAL COMPACT SIZE.

YOU ALREADY HAVE YOUR OWN *SPACECRAFT...*

YES, *YES,* I KNOW!

I WOULD BE VERY SURPRISED IF YOU CLAIMED TO HAVE ONE OF--

THUMPA! THUMPA!

THUMPA! THUMPA!

THUMPA! THUMPA!

49

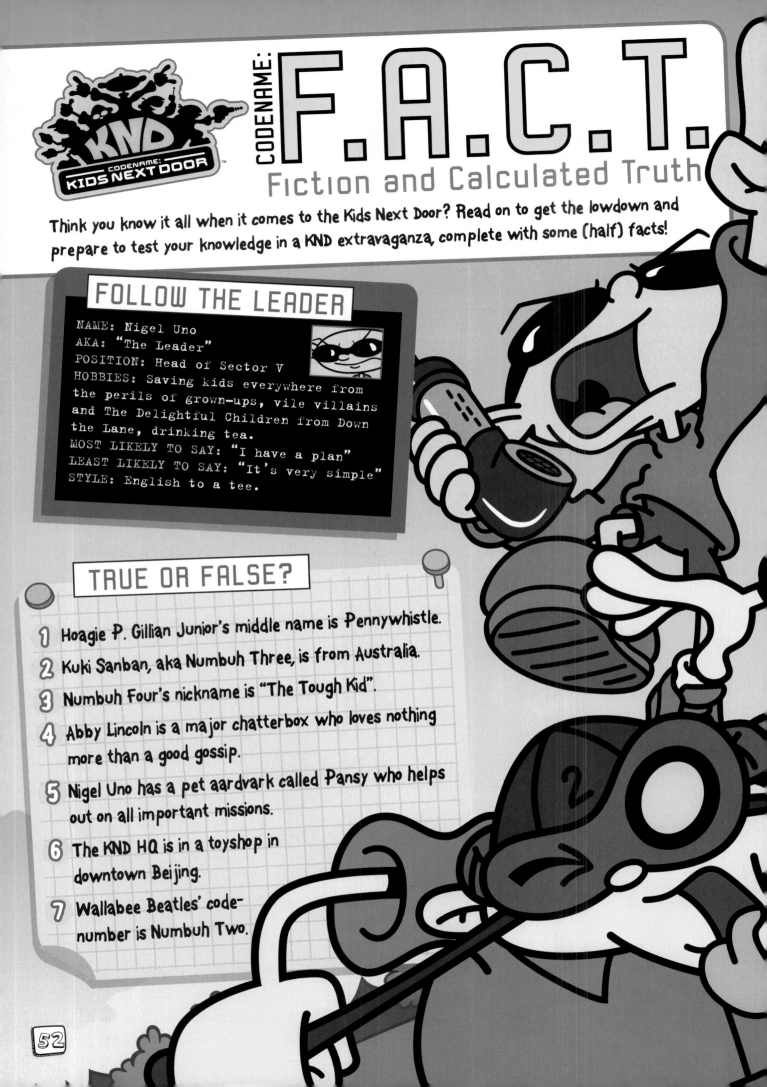

CODENAME: F.A.C.T.
Fiction and Calculated Truth

Think you know it all when it comes to the Kids Next Door? Read on to get the lowdown and prepare to test your knowledge in a KND extravaganza, complete with some (half) facts!

FOLLOW THE LEADER

NAME: Nigel Uno
AKA: "The Leader"
POSITION: Head of Sector V
HOBBIES: Saving kids everywhere from the perils of grown-ups, vile villains and The Delightful Children from Down the Lane, drinking tea.
MOST LIKELY TO SAY: "I have a plan"
LEAST LIKELY TO SAY: "It's very simple"
STYLE: English to a tee.

TRUE OR FALSE?

1. Hoagie P. Gillian Junior's middle name is Pennywhistle.
2. Kuki Sanban, aka Numbuh Three, is from Australia.
3. Numbuh Four's nickname is "The Tough Kid".
4. Abby Lincoln is a major chatterbox who loves nothing more than a good gossip.
5. Nigel Uno has a pet aardvark called Pansy who helps out on all important missions.
6. The KND HQ is in a toyshop in downtown Beijing.
7. Wallabee Beatles' code-number is Numbuh Two.

SEEING DOUBLE

Numbuh Two has been tinkering with the KND S.T.A.N.K. Can you spot the 5 changes that he's made to it?

B

A

FIENDISH FOES

Can you match these ruffians with their descriptions?

VILLAIN: A

VILLAIN: B

VILLAIN: C

VILLAIN: D

VILLAIN: E

VILLAIN: F

1. The Toilenator, the most disgusting villain alive.
2. The Delightful Children from Down the Lane. The KND's arch-enemy.
3. Cree Lincoln, ex-operative turned terrible tyrant.
4. Knightbrace, every kids' biggest fear.
5. Sticky Beard, the candy-munching sea captain.
6. Father - the evil genius of the bothersome bunch.

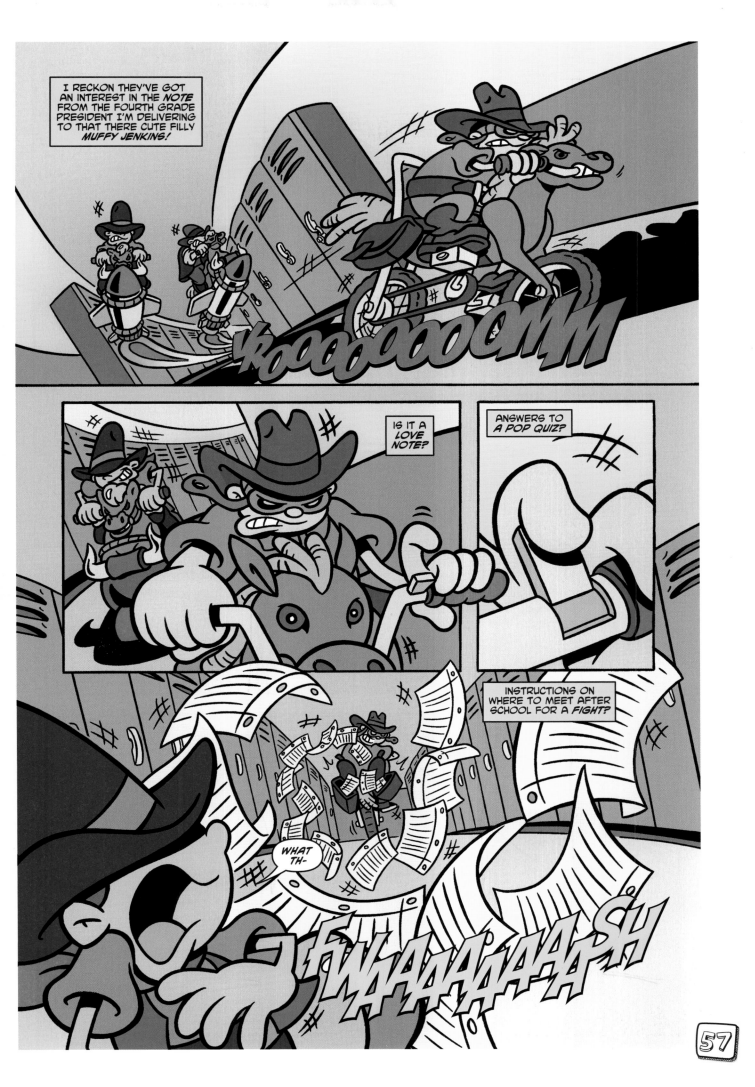

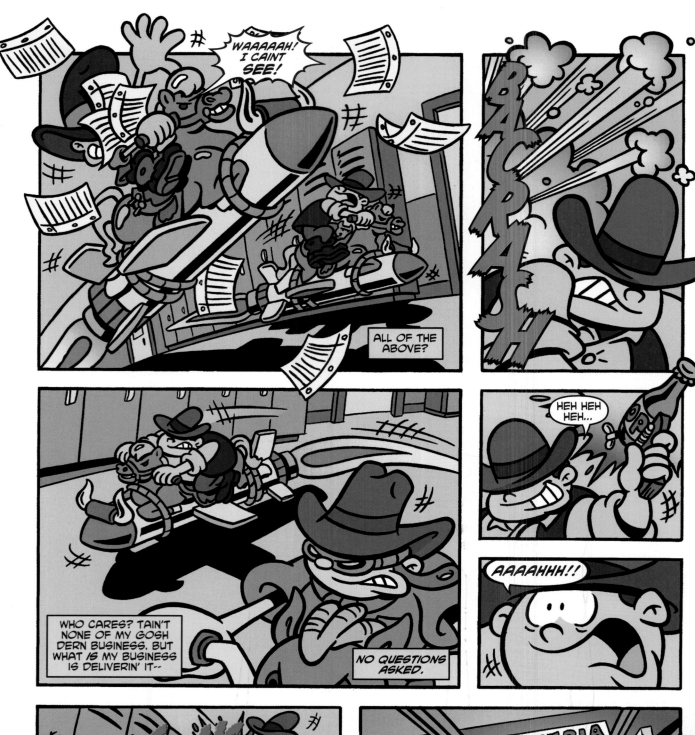

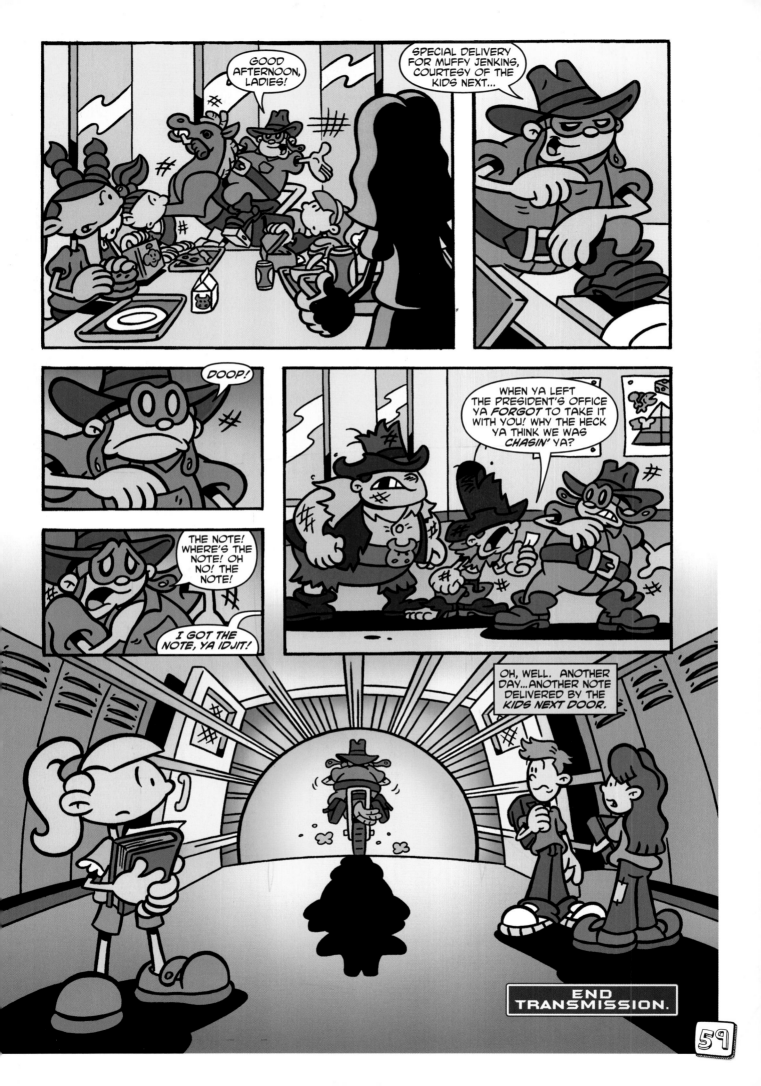

MISSING MATES!

Bloo has managed to trap all of the residents of the Foster's Home for Imaginary Friends in this wordsearch of friendship... Can you help him save them all? Bloo's full name is hidden in the grid too so keep an eye out for it!

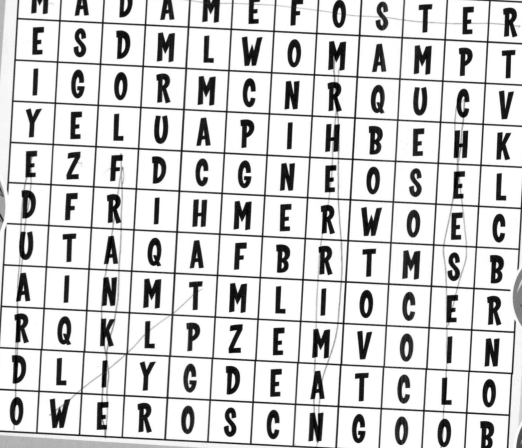

M	A	D	A	M	E	F	O	S	T	E	R
E	S	D	M	L	W	O	M	A	M	P	T
I	G	O	R	M	C	N	R	Q	U	C	V
Y	Y	E	L	U	A	P	I	H	B	E	H	K
E	Z	F	D	C	G	N	E	E	O	S	E	L
D	D	F	R	I	H	M	N	E	R	W	O	M	C
U	T	A	Q	A	F	B	R	T	W	O	M	S	C B
A	I	N	M	T	M	L	I	O	M	C	E	R N
R	Q	K	L	P	Z	E	M	I	O	V	C	I O
D	L	I	Y	G	D	E	A	M	V	T	C	L O
O	W	E	R	O	S	C	N	G	O	O	B

- MADAME FOSTER
- FRANKIE
- EDUARDO
- MAC
- WILT
- CHEESE
- BLOOREGARD
- MR HERRIMAN
- COCO

ANSWERS

21 MENTAL ARTS
LIAR LIAR
The only true answer is number 4.

SAMURAI SKILLS
Samurai Jack wouldn't need: C, D, E, F.

22 PHOTO FINISH
Clam won the race.
The 8 changes are: 1. Raj's neck-tie.
2. Slinkman has one eye. 3. Clam's tongue
has changed colour. 4. Fire. 5. Antlers on
the sign. 6. Lazlo is further behind.
7. Puddles. 8. Clam's horn is missing.

29 EVIL UNITED
Mojo Jojo's evil ally is Him.

31 EDS-TREME THOUGHT
The most profitable money-making scheme is Chores.

32 TASK TIME!
ALIEN ANSWERS

F	O	U	R	A	R	M	S	T	G	D
K	8	G	A	R	F	E	N	T	R	I
A	T	P	9	S	2	L	S	U	6	A
E	I	W	C	H	U	5	W	M	A	M
R	I	P	J	A	W	E	K	D	H	O
F	4	L	U	N	I	3	F	L	Y	N
T	D	H	L	R	8	Q	E	I	S	D
S	O	M	J	Z	B	K	I	W	I	H
O	7	E	D	A	R	G	P	U	X	E
H	E	A	T	B	L	A	S	T	O	A
G	R	E	Y	M	A	T	T	E	R	D

WATCH IT!
The missing alien DNA is Ghostfreak

41 MEGA MIX-UP!
IN BITS!
The parts which don't belong to
MEGAS are: F and H.

IN DISGUISE
The true XLR is number 2.

44 CHEMICAL CHAOS!
MISTAKEN IDENTITY
The 7 differences are: 1. DeeDee's dress. 2. DeeDee's
leg stripes. 3. Mandark's ties. 4. Mandark's teddy. 5.
Dexter's eyes. 6. DeeDee's tongue. 7. Dexter's hair.

THE BIG BANG!
The only two chemicals which can be mixed are
yellow and blue.

52 OPERATION F.A.C.T.
TRUE OR FALSE
1. True. 2. False. 3. True. 4. False. 5. False. 6.
False. 7. False.

SEEING DOUBLE
The changes are:
1. Wheel. 2. Missing propeller.
3. No KND writing. 4. Pink
bumper. 5. Numbuh Three in
the vehicle.

60 MISSING MATES

M	A	D	A	M	E	F	O	S	T	E	R
E	S	D	M	L	W	O	M	A	M	P	T
I	G	O	R	M	C	N	R	Q	U	C	V
Y	E	L	U	A	P	I	H	B	E	N	K
E	Z	F	D	C	N	E	O	S	E	E	L
D	F	R	I	H	M	E	R	W	O	E	C
U	T	A	Q	A	F	B	R	T	M	C	K
I	N	I	T	M	L	I	O	S	E	G	E
R	Q	K	L	P	Z	E	N	V	D	I	I
D	L	Y	I	G	D	E	A	T	C	L	O
O	W	E	F	R	O	S	C	N	G	O	O